CATS

By Caroline and John Astrop

Firefly

Here are three baby cats.
What are baby cats called?
Which two look the same?

The naughty kittens are hiding.
Can you find them?

Find the right tail for each animal.

China cat has a blue tail.
Have you got a tail?
What other animal has a tail?

These cats make a terrible noise.
Can you meow, very loudly?
Can you meow, very quietly?

Find the quiet cats and the noisy cats.

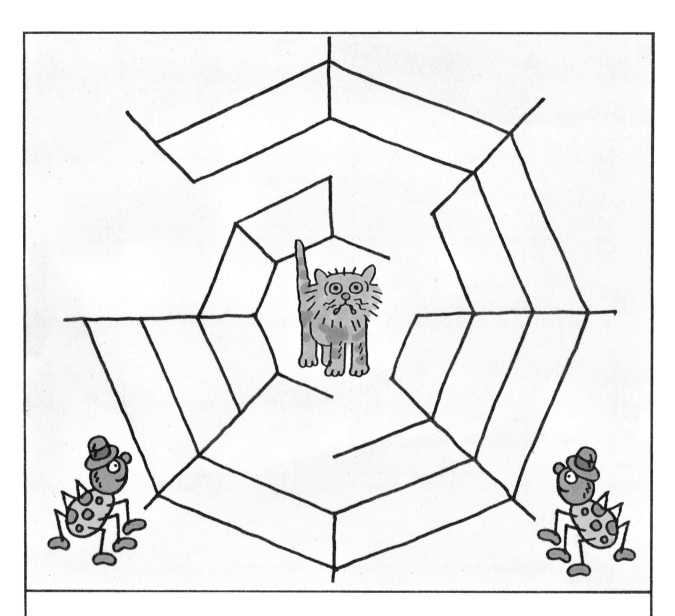

Can you show scaredy cat the way out?

Scaredy cat is frightened of something.
What has frightened him?
What things frighten you?

This cat is in a cradle.
What kind of bed do you sleep in?
What toy do you take to bed with you?

Which are the bed-time things?

These cats are fishing. What have they caught?

Hungry cat only has fishbones.
Where did he find them?
What would you give him to eat?

Happy cat laps milk with her tongue.
Can you drink milk like a cat?
Can you purr like a happy cat?

Point to the happy cats.

Which chair should this fat cat sit on?

Two old cats.
Which one is the fattest?
Which one is smiling?

Puppet cat has long whiskers.
How many has she got?
Can you see a curly one?

Can you spot the differences?

Which cat is dressed for dancing?

The dancing cat loves music.
Can you dance to music?
What colour is his jacket?

Here are some of the words you have learned in this book

three · cats · same

china · animal · tail

chorus · loudly · quietly

cradle · bed · sleep

scaredy · cat · frighten

hungry · fishbones · caught

laps · tongue · purr

two · old · fattest

puppet · whiskers · curly

dancing · music · jacket

Hardback edition first published in the UK in 1989 by
Firefly Books Limited
61, Western Road, Hove
East Sussex BN3 1JD, England

British Library Cataloguing in Publication Data
Astrop, Caroline
Cats.
1. Cats – For children
I. Title   II. Astrop, John   III. Series
636.8

ISBN 1 85485 019 9

Typeset by Type Practitioners, Sevenoaks, Kent
Printed in Italy

CHATTERBOOKS